ANIMALS HAVE LOTS OF FUN

ANIMALS HAVE LOTS OF FUN

By Jiří Havel
Translated by Stephen Finn
Illustrated by Karel Franta

TREASURE PRESS

First published 1986 by
Treasure Press
59 Grosvenor Street
London, Wl
Reprinted 1987
Graphic design by Miroslav Habr
Copyright © Artia, Prague 1986
ISBN 1 85051 067 9
Printed in Czechoslovakia by Severografia, Liberec
1/05/24/51-02

CONTENTS

I'm dreadfully inquisitive,
And can't stay put for long.
And if I could, I'd like to live
Somewhere out there among
The animals. Well, wouldn't you?
But anyway, I've been
Along to visit one or two.
I'll tell you what I've seen ...

THE CATS' HOUSE

Can you hear that dreadful row?
Guess what they are up to now;
Fancy a family of cats
Putting up a block of flats!

They're going to make it a whopping great place,
Where even the kits'll have plenty of space;
With different colours on different floors,
And a room in the cellar for washing their paws.

There'll be electric lights as well,
And at the door a golden bell,
Beside a notice to declare
That dogs are not allowed in there.

But the thing which is really attracting a crowd
Is something of which they're especially proud.
It's a little loud-squeaker, for talking to mice,
That keeps saying: 'Come in, dears — it's terribly
nice!'

HOPEFUL TOMMY

'You naughty little kitten!
Wherever have you been?
That's quite the blackest tummy
That I have ever seen!'

'I was playing by the garage,'
Wailed Tommy, in distress,
And Mummy said: 'No wonder
Your coat's in such a mess!

'But still, it's no use crying,
'Cause tears won't save the day.
I haven't got another
To give you, anyway.'

But little Tommy told her:
'I know what I shall do —
If I call at the dry-cleaners
It'll be as good as new!'

ALWAYS A FIRST TIME...

Underneath the table,
Lying where they fell,
The cat found Grandad's glasses;
The rest is sad to tell.

Pussy soon decided
That spectacles must be
Just great for hunting mice with,
And so she went to see...

Peering in the mousehole,
She had an awful scare:
She spotted quite distinctly
A monster mouse in there.

Mice will long remember
That historic day,
And like to tell the tale of
The cat that ran away!

OUR FLYING CAT

There's not a mouse in all the house,
Of that you can be sure.
The other day we found a way
To drive them from the door.

They lived up in the garret,
But don't go near it now,
Since father bought a parrot
And taught it to miaow!

THE MICE'S BALL

Tonight's the night at the granary hall,
The mice are holding their annual ball!

There'll be field mice and house mice and
                white mice and brown,
And rich mice and church mice from county and town.
There'll be music and dancing from dusk until dawn,
But the best fun will be when the raffle is drawn!
Then the dancers are certain to crowd round the stage,
'Cause they're giving the winner A CAT IN A CAGE!

THERE'S NOTHING TO IT!

'Sometime,' said Puss, 'I'd like to learn that song —
The one you dogs keep singing all day long.'
'Why not,' said Fido. 'I can teach you now:
The first word's *bow*, and all the rest are *wow*.'

MEET THE GANG

Come and meet my canine friends;
I'm sure you'll get on well,
Though how they'll take to strangers
It's difficult to tell.

For no two dogs are quite alike,
From lapdogs down to strays,
And one will bark, another bite,
While one just sits and bays.
Then some are long, and others short,
And some have hairy faces.
There's one or two that put on airs,
But others know their places.

On one thing, though, we're all agreed,
Whatever shape or size or breed,
A rule that has to be obeyed:
Our masters mustn't be betrayed!

LONG LIVE GRASS!

The grass in the meadow helps Daisy the cow
To give us a calf, though I'm not quite sure how.
The calf will grow bigger and give us another,
So isn't the grass really some sort of mother?

COW MAGIC

The humble cow's a magic thing,
Of that there is no doubt.
However else could grass go in
And milk and cream come out?

ROSIE THE GOAT

Do you suppose
The farmer knows
Of Rosie's shopping trips?
With painted toes
And powdered nose
And lipstick on her lips?

On Saturday
She sneaks away
And minces off to town.
And there she'll stay,
Or so they say,
Until the sun goes down.

It's funny, though,
Not long ago
She ruined her fancy clothes.
She stubbed her toe
Upon a hoe
And fell flat on her nose!

POOR BILLY

'Like Lucifer!' the people say.
He hates it — wouldn't you?
It isn't his fault. Anyway,
It's not entirely true.

Perhaps a devil's horns and chin,
And devil's tail and feet.
But what about the rest of him?
Besides — do devils bleat?

ALWAYS A CATCH

Alas! The foolish little fly:
As in the honey jar he fell,
'How sweet life is!' they heard him cry.
It was. But it was short as well.

HARD WORK

It's only through the patience
Of millions of sheep
We can make the calculations
That get us off to sleep.

AN EARLY MORNING DIP

A cloudless day was dawning
In just that sort of way
That gives the world a warning:
'You're going to fry today!'

Willie Wasp was worried
In case there was a queue,
So he got up and hurried
To get his share of dew.

Each time he found a flower
Full up to the brim,
He either took a shower
Or dived in for a swim!

THE BEE

With pollen for powder, the wind for a comb,
The dew for a mirror, the world for a home,
The sun on her wings, and all of it free,
It must be quite wonderful being a bee.

22

A GOOD EDUCATION

The parrot's swotting French and Greek,
Italian, Spanish and what not;
He's not content to learn to speak —
He wants to be a Polly-glot.

THE MODEST DONKEY

There's just one thing that worries me,
That's whether I should go to school.
I can't think if I'd rather be
A clever ass, or just a fool!

A BAD WORKMAN . . .

The butterfly, who'd bumped his head,
Kicked his skipping-rope, and said:
'Here's the thing that made me trip —
The stupid thing forgot to skip!'

SWEET DREAMS

'Butterfly, with wings so bright,
Tell us where you sleep at night.'

'Every evening I alight
On the prettiest flower in sight.
When I wake up it always seems
Like I've been having scented dreams.'

THE MUSICIAN

He'll play a merry dancing tune
For flies that flit about the glade,
But when it's dark and there's no moon,
He plays a simple serenade.

TIT FOR TAT

A certain little wasp espied
A blackbird, drinking at the spring,
'How come,' the cheeky insect cried,
'You don't have feelers or a sting?'
'I'll tell you that,' the bird replied,
'As soon as you have learned to sing!'

WHAT CHEEK!

As I stepped out one morning,
Sleepy and still yawning,
I saw a mole
Just climbing from his hole.

I said: 'I beg your pardon,
Who let you in the garden?'
He turned around
And made another mound.

I came back with the skinner:
The mole had gone to dinner.
He'd left his spade
Beside the mess he'd made.

A FISH FEUD

I know when, but I'm not sure how;
A pair of fishes had a row.

From that day forth — or so I've heard —
They've not exchanged another word.

The reason hasn't been revealed,
The other fishes' lips are sealed.

THOSE CRAZY CRAYFISH

Why is the crayfish frowning so?
Actually, I think I know.

26

He's writing fairy tales again.
It really must be quite a strain,
Since — or at least, so people say —
He writes a dozen every day.
He has to rack his clever brain
To tell each one a different way,
And still make sure the final line
Is always 'once upon a time'.
The reason's really very sound,
For crayfish read the wrong way round!

WHERE?

Where would a hare in the wood comb his hair,
If comb his hair he could?
If only a hare could comb his hair,
He'd comb it in the wood!

28

WHY FROGS DON'T WEAR SWIMMING COSTUMES

The frogs once thought it would be great
To organize a swimming fête,
And soon announced their firm intent
To hold an annual event.

Mamma collected lots of scales
Fallen from the fishes' tails,
And sewed them up with ragwort roots,
To make some shiny swimming suits.

Before the races could begin,
They had to practise diving in,
And trainer Green had lots of fun
Demonstrating how it's done.

Then they lined up in a row,
And Green said: 'Ready, steady, go!'
But scarcely had they swum a stroke,
Before the coach began to croak:

'Look out, look out, the stork is here!
It's time for us to disappear!'
The racers fled, and Green the coach
Sold their swimsuits to the roach.

They still have races every year,
But now the storks don't venture near.
They think the frogs are rather rude
To do their swimming in the nude.

FULL MARKS FOR TRYING

Bruin's busy — have you heard?
He wants to warble like a bird;
Won't stop trying, even though
The whole idea is quite absurd.
He should have realized long ago
Something any fool should know,
That, quite apart from other things,
He'll never warble without wings.

30

FIRST THINGS FIRST

Even March hares, come September,
Are obliged to go to school,
Where they teach them to remember
This important rhyming rule:
'Though carrots may be gently crunched,
Cabbage should be quietly munched.'

WOODLAND SONG

When little birds are growing up,
The most important thing
Is for them to learn to listen
Before they learn to sing.

32

To listen to the music
Of the gentle forest breeze,
As it swishes through the bushes
And ripples through the trees.

They learn by heart the chorus
Of that windy woodland song,
And then they know exactly
When they should sing along.

THE BLUSHING FOX

The sun was beating on the glade,
The air was hot and hazy.
The vixen lay down in the shade,
Feeling rather lazy.

It made the spruce tree quite irate
To see the vixen slacking,
And so he shouted: 'Just you wait!
I'll see you get a whacking!

'Such indolence is a disgrace!'
And he hurled his cones right at her.
The vixen raised a smiling face,
As if it didn't matter.

'How right you are, you wise old tree!'
She told him, before going.
'I'm quite ashamed — why, can't you see
How very red I'm growing?'

CAN'T SAY FAIRER THAN THAT

The crow exclaimed: 'That piece of cheese
Is full of holes, now if you please...'
The fox replied: 'You silly crow!
That's Emmenthal — you ought to know

It's meant to have the holes in it;
They're actually the nicest bit.
But I don't mind leaving them for you,
For a humble fox, the cheese will do!'

POOR DESIGN

Said a certain young adder on shedding his skin:
'It's much worse getting out than it was getting in.
These coats would be very much simpler to strip
If they'd only remember to put in a zip!'

HERBIE'S ADVENTURE

Herbie the Hedgehog went out for a walk,
Across to the woodland glade.
At twilight the forest grew dreadfully dark,
And Herbie became afraid.

He burst into tears and curled up in a heap,
And didn't know what to do.
A spruce spread its branches and said: 'Go to sleep;
I'm here to look after you.'

When Father went out on the following day,
He found him beneath the tree.
The lad was just lying there, snoring away,
Content as content could be!

A BEAR'S WORK

Daddy Bear gets up at ten
And eats a tub of honey.
Puts his big fur coat on, then
Goes out to earn some money.

Until noon he does his rounds
Among the shrubs and creepers,
Laying false trails for the hounds
And frightening gamekeepers.

After lunch he goes to bed,
All bleary-eyed and yawning;
There he rests his weary head
Till ten o'clock next morning.

But baby bears are up at eight
In kind or cruel weather,
And if the fox-cubs are not late
They go to school together.

For even Daddy Bear once went
To school, to be enlightened
On how a dog's put off the scent
And gamekeepers are frightened.

AT YOUR SERVICE

Through the trees the morning breeze
Was silently but swiftly sweeping;
It told the bear: 'I'll comb your hair —
Or would you rather go on sleeping?'

Bruno grunted: 'Comb away —
I'm having visitors today.'

JUST LIKE HOME

Not long ago a cousin paid
A call on Bruno in his lair,
And asked for ice-cold lemonade.
He is, you see, a polar bear.

THE NIGHT WATCH

What excellent care the owlets took
Of the forest on Saturday night!
At quarter-past nine they had a look,
And they hooted that it was all right;
But then they just read a story book,
With the help of the moon's silver light.

NOT TO WORRY

'I think the lion's cross with me,'
Said Tommy Turtle, timidly.
He added, hiding in his shell:
'It's all because I run so well!'

HIPPO PRANKS

Hippo-pota-muses don't like doing sums,
So they're often very naughty just before the teacher comes.
Rowdy hippo boys begin to barge and bump,
And they tease the hippo girls, and even kick them in the rump!

But those hippo-pota-misses don't bother answering
'Cos through their hefty hippo hides they never feel a thing.

44

THE CROCODILES' PICNIC

What a day out for the crocodile quins!
Father was taking them all for a swim.
Up to the waterfall, down to the lake,
Think what a wonderful trip it would make!

Soon they got hungry and said: 'Deary me,
I wonder what Mother is making for tea?'
Wasn't it lucky that, on the way back,
They met some explorers, and stopped for a snack?

THE WASTEFUL WHALE

The whale's a very wasteful beast
And never thrifty in the least;
For him a simple bath won't do —
He has to have a shower too!
Children, don't you think he oughta
Try to save a little water?

SEA SWEATERS

The cormorant is sure he knows
Where all that seething sea-foam goes.
He says the whales collect it all
And roll it up into a ball
For grandma whales, so they can knit
The children jumpers out of it.

NO DEAL

The zebra asked the rainbow:
'Do you suppose we might
Change our stripes? For mine are dull,
And yours are nice and bright!'

The rainbow told the zebra:
'My dear, it's only right
That I was made in colour
And you in black and white.

'Because if things were different
You'd make a pretty sight.
But then, the lions and leopards
Could hunt you day and night!'

A GOOD REASON

Of course, it's not a bit of use
My telling the zebra twins
They must get dressed.
They've got a very good excuse
For wearing pyjama skins
Like all the rest!

A SPECIAL TREAT

The baby giraffes gave a shout of glee,
And opened their little eyes wide,
When Mum said that after they'd had their tea
They could use her long neck as a slide.

JUST LIKE AN ELEPHANT!

Poor Jumbo's feeling rather glum,
For while out walking with his mum,
He somehow managed, if you please,
To trap his trunk between his knees.
It wasn't really Jumbo's fault;
He turned a lovely somersault,
But landed with an awful bump,
And Mother said: 'You are a chump!'

WHY KNOT?

For an elephant, Bimbo was terribly good
At forgetting to do all the things that he should,
So whenever his mum sent him somewhere, he knew
He must do something clever to give him a clue.
He remembered to fasten his trunk in a knot,
But the reason he'd done it — he promptly forgot!

A GOOD IDEA

Each and every summer's day
Bimbo's at the pool,
He knows a very simple way
To keep the children cool!

BAD NEWS

This piece of news is rather bad
And sure to make you very sad,
For Bimbo left the local fair
With five balloons he'd purchased there.
The way he went was somewhat weird —
He just took off, and disappeared!

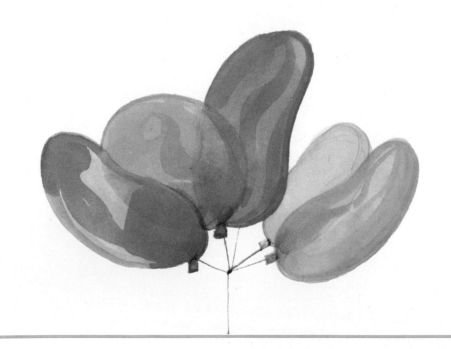

POOR KANGAROO

Kim's been a naughty kangaroo,
As he's inclined to be.
So Daddy said he'd have to go
To pouch, without his tea!

PUTTING ON A SHOW

What happens at monkey drama school?
The answer is easily found.
The one in the middle plays the fool
While the rest of them monkey around!

NO JOKE

They wouldn't live in houses,
But if they had some money
At least they'd buy some trousers.
'Cos they think that if they'd got 'em
They wouldn't look as funny
As they do with a bare bottom!

A NEW FASHION

The camel's quite contented
And doesn't care who knows,
Because he's just invented
The latest thing in clothes.

It's really rather simple,
A hat that has two bumps,
And in between a dimple,
To fit a camel's humps.

WHAT A CHORE!

A camel's life is not much fun;
It's awful when you think
He spends the whole day in the sun,
And seldom gets a drink.

His working life he's forced to spend
In a hot and dusty land,
Roaming it from end to end
And counting all the sand.

It must be such an awful bore:
He counts it grain by grain,
Until his eyes are red and sore —
Then counts it all again!

A MAN'S WORK

Female ostriches would rather
Leave incubation to the father.

Daddy doesn't mind a bit,
In fact, he's very good at it.

ROYAL VANITY

The lion's grown extremely vain,
And creatures come in scores
To see how he shampoos his mane,
And manicures his claws.

A STAR IN THE MAKING

When lion cubs have learned to roar
They like to prove it proudly,
And do it daily more and more
And always much too loudly.

But Mum and Dad don't seem to care,
In fact, their great ambition
Is to find a cub who has a flair,
And get him an audition.

For if a lion's voice is good
And his expression toothy,
He might make it to Hollywood,
And introduce a movie!

AT THE ZOO

Hoppity, skippity, down to the zoo,
Just to find out if it really was true.
Who'd have believed it? I'd scarcely got in
When I spotted a bear with gills on his chin.
Not far away was a silly old seal,
Nibbling her trunk — how strange it must feel!
The sea-lion was having a treat on that day,
Peeling bananas and munching away.
Over his cage, with a warbling song,
A lesser-striped donkey came flying along.

The jackal was making a terrible din,
Flailing about with his gigantic fin.
Hissing, an elephant slid through the grass
Just as a leopard came lolloping past,
Carrying two little cubs in its pouch.
'What are you doing? You're hurting me! Ouch!'
Twittered the ass to a mischievous fox
That was nibbling a piece out of one of her socks.
Tossed by a wolf, I came down to the ground,
And just missed a camel, who, turning around,
Pointed its antlers to where, up above,
A lion was fluttering about like a dove.

As I was just about ready to go,
I met a young lioness who I know,
Standing there quietly under a tree,
Singing as loudly as loudly can be.
Just for a moment she stood and she stared,
Wiggling her humps; then she sternly declared:

'A proper little monkey *you* are!'
(Didn't she go just a little too far?)

Really a terrible thing to say;
So, turning and facing the opposite way,
I stood and looked at her, straight in the eyes;
Imagine a lioness telling such lies!

Now I've told you all I saw,
And maybe just a little more.
I know some of the tales were tall,
But I hope that you've enjoyed them all.
Perhaps we'll meet again sometime
To study animals in rhyme,
And then we'll really do our best
To take a look at all the rest.